Within the pages of this Holo-book, you will meet and interact with the officers of the 88th Precinct. From logging on over the page, you will be enrolled as a Cadet and given the chance to test your strength and skills in this dangerous future environment. Good luck!

£5.25

urgent spaceMAIL message from
@InterPlanetPol.SP88.bqww:

+++ Congratulations, you have been accepted from thousands of applicants all over the galaxy for enrollment as a cadet police officer in the Mentorn System. You will be assigned to the 88th Precinct on the Planet Altor for training and all aspects of your performance will be assessed carefully.

+++ Your initial tour of duty will last for one month, during which time you will be expected to carry out the regular work of a police officer in Demeter City - considered by many to be the crime capital of the galaxy! If you survive that month, your cadet's badge will be renewed for further training.

+++ During your time at the Space Precinct, you will be continually briefed on how to survive in Demeter and you are urged to seek advice from more experienced colleagues. They may have to rely on you in a dangerous situation, so be assured that they'll be keen for you to learn very fast!

+++ You are required to report to the 88th Precinct right away. Your training will begin immediately after you have entered your personal details into the file opposite. It will begin with a short tour of the Precinct itself, then anything could happen, and it probably will. Good luck, Cadet - you're going to need it!

+++ MESSAGE ENDS

Bio-File

SCROLL IN

NAME: Matthew Nix

Rank: Cadet

Serial No: DCPD HTEMP96

Species: HUMAN

Home:

Trainee Housing, Demeter City

Age: 8

Planet of origin: EARTH

Home Town: Brix waren

School: Maidwell

Affix picture here

© 1995 The Space Precinct Limited Partnership. All rights reserved. Licensed by Mentorn Films / Gerry Anderson. Published by Grandreams Limited, Jadwin House, 205 / 211 Kentish Town, London, NW5 2JU. Printed in Italy.

MENTORN Films

SPACE PRECINCT
OFFICIAL LICENSED PRODUCT
DEMETER CITY POLICE DEPARTMENT

5

Welcome to the 88th Precinct! If you don't know much about Altor and the Mentorn System, then you needn't worry. You'll be fully briefed during your training here at the Precinct, as well as being introduced to all our key personnel - including the officers you are likely to be working with. You will have to concentrate, however, because any piece of information could be vital to your survival here in Demeter City and you will also be severely tested at the end of your training. So listen up, Cadet, your inauguration begins here...

An orbiting Station House

Demeter City's 88th Precinct Station House has all the facilities you would expect of similar establishment on earth. With officers, criminal interview rooms, holding cells and even docking bays for a fleet of police cruisers, a Space Precinct is fully equipped to combat crime. Situated in orbit high above the surface of Altor, the Station House is also one of the most secure.

Staffed by humans, aliens and other lifeforms!

There are a number of human police officers working out of Precinct 88, like Lieutenant Brogan, Officer Haldane, Officer Castle and the Precinct's Science Officer Carson. Most of the remaining cops are either tarns or creons and everyone relies on the Space Precinct's robotic "gofer", Slomo. You will be more fully introduced to all of your colleagues during your training.

Your bosses and other aliens

The 88th Precinct is run by the creon Captain Podly who is assisted by his reliable tarn deputy, Sergeant Fredo. Another tarn you are likely to meet is the sensitive Officer Took, while there are several creons you should look out for. Officers Orrin and Romek usually work together.

Manual Memory

ALTOR

Although it is a small planet, the strategic importance of Altor cannot be underestimated. Situated in a key position in the Mentorn System - a solar system similar to earth's on a spiral arm of the Milky Way - Altor is a major refuelling stop for interplantery freight.
Coupled with a special treaty with earth, this resulted in the planet's population increasing very rapidly, as aliens - particularly creons and tarns - sought a new life there. Demeter City is Altor's capital and main population centre - a crowded multi-cultural society divided into countless alien communities. The largest of these remain the tarn and creon groups, but the human population is growing fast. Altor's economy is firmly based on trade and many intergalactic businesses have offices there. The planet's relative prosperity is balanced by the high rate of crime there - something the Demeter City Police Department does is best to remedy!

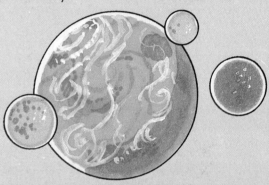

SURVIVAL TIP: YOU MUST LEARN TO BE ADAPTABLE WHEN YOU'RE ON ALTOR - ITS MULTICULTURAL SOCIETY GIVES IT THE MOST STRANGE AND EXCITING ENVIRONMENT IN THE GALAXY.

SIMTER

The ancestral home of all tarns, Simter is one of Altor's neighbouring planets. Although it is basically a peaceful planet, life is hard on Simter. Trading opportunities are few and the place is not rich with natural resources. Consequently, many tarns emigrated to Altor and those who remained were a tough breed, proud of their home planet.

SURVIVAL TIP: OUTSIDERS ARE NOT ALWAYS WELCOME ON SIMTER, SO ENSURE THAT YOU ARE WELL AWARE OF ALL THE LOCAL TARNS' CUSTOMS BEFORE SETTING FOOT ON THEIR PLANET.

DANAE

A chaotic and poverty-stricken planet, it is no wonder that creons left Danae in droves when they had the chance to pursue considerably brighter trading opportunities on Altor. Danae has a long-standing rivalry with its neighbour Simter and that rivalry continues as both worlds strive to take advantage of the Mentorn System's increasing prominence in the Galaxy

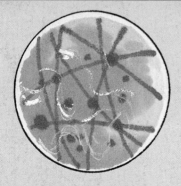

SURVIVAL TIP: DANAE CAN BE A CONFUSING AND BEWILDERING PLACE FOR OFF WORLDERS AND THE LOCAL CONMEN ARE WELL KNOWN FOR TAKING ADVANTAGE OF UNSUSPECTING VISITORS.

SAGANIA

Coming from a society torn apart by political divisions and civil war, many Saganians seek refuge off world. They are very humanoid in appearance, but often find it hard to find new homes in a sometimes unfriendly universe.

SURVIVAL TIP: ENSURE YOU HAVE ALL THE CORRECT DOCUMENTS IF YOU HAVE TO VISIT SAGANIA. IF YOU LACK THE PROPER ENTRY AND EXIT VISAS YOU MAY NEVER GET HOME AGAIN!

MELAZOID ONE

A busy and relatively prosperous world, Melazoid One has strong business links with Altor. As their appearance and habits are repugnant to most other races, Melazoids have to work hard to win the confidence of their associates.

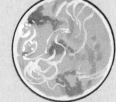

SURVIVAL TIP: DESPITE THEIR APPEARANCE, MOST MELAZOIDS ARE FRIENDLY AND LAW-ABIDING. WHATEVER YOU DO, THOUGH, DON'T ACCEPT AN INVITATION TO ONE OF THEIR FLY-SLURPING PARTIES!

ASTEROID A5

Also known as "The Rock", Asteroid A5 is a maximum security prison used by the DCPD. Reserved for the most dangerous and vicious criminals, The Rock is purported to be the most escape-proof and toughest jail in the Galaxy.

SURVIVAL TIP: ALWAYS APPROACH THE ROCK WITH CAUTION. DESPITE ITS REPUTATION, BREAK-OUTS ARE NOT ACTUALLY UNKNOWN AND YOU DON'T WANT TO MEET ANY OF ITS INMATES.

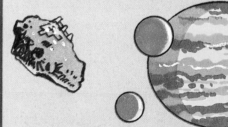

NEVIN THREE

Nevin Three is situated far out in the rim worlds. Populated by a proud race called the Ulred, the planet has been reduced to civil war by the Omera, an evil nomadic race dedicated to conquering the entire universe!

SURVIVAL TIP: LITTLE IS KNOWN ABOUT MANY OF THE RIM WORLDS, SO IF YOUR DUTY TAKES YOU TO SOMEWHERE LIKE NEVIN THREE MAKE SURE YOU INFORM THE LEAGUE OF PLANETS FIRST.

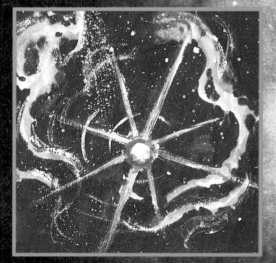

Avalon/Miracles Inc.

Meet your colleagues:

PATRICK BROGAN
BIO-FILE

Rank: **Lieutenant**
Serial No: **DCPD H5323M**
Species: **Human**
Home: **Space Suburb**

A born leader and an excellent detective

Brogan is a senior cop with more than two decades' experience so you're sure to find him a valuable friend and colleague when you have to patrol the dangerous streets of Demeter City. Watch out though, Cadet, Lieutenant Brogan expects very high standards of his fellow officers - so be prepared for a rough ride if you make too many mistakes!

SCROLL IN

Recently transferred from the New York Police Department

Brogan was born and raised in New York and served with the NYPD for twenty years before seeking a new challenge at the 88th Precinct. He volunteered for an exchange programme with the Demeter City Police Department - that's right, he volunteered for this assignment just like you did, so at least you have one thing in common with the Lieutenant.

Dedicated to the truth and determined to succeed

Willing to accept responsibility for even the most difficult of investigations, Brogan detests having to leave any case unsolved. His determination to uncover the truth sometimes leads him into danger, so you might find yourself having to watch his back. Brogan often seems to be on a short fuse, but don't be too intimidated, Cadet, he has a keen sense of humour, too.

FREEZE FRAME

A good husband and a proud father

Brogan moved to Altor with his wife Sally, a post-trauma therapist specialising in alien post-operative care, their 12 year old daughter Liz and 15 year old son Matt. They have recently acquired one further family member - their alien pet Zil. Brogan is a stern but compassionate father and regrets that his job means he can't spend as much time with his family as he would like.

Home from home in the Space Suburb

To make their new environment a bit easier for his family to get used to, Brogan arranged for many of their earth possessions to be transported to Altor. With all these familiar items installed in their apartment, the Brogans' home in the huge orbiting Space Suburb Delta is a constant reminder of earth in the middle of a friendly - but to them, alien - community.

VR QUIZ

To prepare you for the ordeals you are likely to face as a police officer in Demeter City, Sergeant Fredo has arranged for a short VR patrol simulation to be fitted into your briefing schedule. In this simulation you will be partnered by the tarn officer Took, as you take your police cruiser downtown.

1. Your cruiser is flagged down by a shifty looking creon. Took stops the vehicle and you get out to speak to the man. He tells you that he has some information concerning a snuff fight, but he wants you to pay him for it. How do you react to his request?
(a) Arrest him for trying to con you out of money.
(b) Check his status with Precinct 88.
(c) Offer him half what he's asking for the same information.

2. You pursue a lead to a rundown tenement building. Your information takes you to a corridor where there are three doors, each of which has what appears to be a name written on it. Can you decide which one has something to do with the organ leggers you are looking for?
(a) ROGLY PLANKTON
(b) SPIROL LEGGIST
(c) SEGOL GRANGER

3. You've worked out which is the correct door. What do you do next?
(a) Knock the door politely and wait for a reply.
(b) Smash the door down and race in to try and make an arrest!
(c) Announce that you're a police officer and ask them to open the door.

4. You enter the room carefully, but it is empty apart from a few surgical items and a large notebook, confirming that you are in the right place. As you open the door you hear a faint beeping sound. How do you react?
(a) Grab the notebook and get out of there quickly.
(b) Conduct a thorough search of the room.
(c) Ask Officer Took what she thinks the noise could be?

5. Took makes sure you get clear of the room as an explosion set off by the door alarm destroys the evidence inside. Fortunately, you have the notebook and find lots of names and addresses inside. There are three separate lists in the book,

which one will you check out first?
(a) The one with crosses beside the names.
(b) The shortest one with no marks at all near the names.
(c) The one with numbers beside the names.

6. You track down a human, who is the top name on the list of organ leggers in the notebook. He denies everything. What is your next step?
(a) Take him back to the Precinct for interrogation.
(b) Ask Took to try and read his mind with her third eye.
(c) Let him go.

7. The man finally admits his guilt, but you need to incriminate all of his accomplices in order to close down the organ legging operation. You are back at the Precinct and another officer offers you a helping hand. He attacks the criminal violently, warning him that he will beat the information out of him if he has to. What do you do while he does this?
(a) Report the officer to the Captain.
(b) Join in.
(c) Watch carefully and pick up some interrogation tips.

8. Once the rest of the organ leggers have been arrested, Captain Podly calls you into his office and tears you off a strip for all the mistakes you made during the investigation. How do you respond?
(a) Say nothing.
(b) Thank him for his comments and vow to do better next time.
(c) Tell him he should be grateful - after all, you did catch the bad guys.

⊛ ASSESSMENT

1. (a) 0 points, **(b)** 5 points, **(c)** 2 points
2. (a) 0, **(b)** 0, **(c)** 5 - it's an anagram of organ leggers!
3. (a) 2, **(b)** 0, **(c)** 5
4. (a) 5, **(b)** 0, **(c)** 2
5. (a) 0 - victims, **(b)** 5 - culprits, **(c)** 2 - clients
6. (a) 2, **(b)** 5, **(c)** 0
7. (a) 5, **(b)** 0, **(c)** 0
8. (a) 2, **(b)** 5, **(c)** 0

⊛ RATINGS

0-10: What a crock! Let's hope you make out better during the rest of your training, Cadet, otherwise it's pretty unlikely you're going to survive long enough to earn yourself a space cop's badge.
11-30: You tried hard, but you'll need to sharpen your reactions and work on your judgement to make the grade. Everyone's rooting for you, though, so get out there and show us what you can really do!
31-40: Excellent, you've made a terrific impression with the Captain and your other colleagues. This is the kind of start most cadets can only dream of - so make sure you don't blow it during the rest of your training.

JACK HALDANE
BIO-FILE

Rank: Officer
Serial No: DCPD H5324M
Species: Human
Home: Space Suburb

From Tennessee to New York to Demeter City

When Jack Haldane left school in Tennessee he headed off to New York looking for adventure. Partnering our very own Patrick Brogan in the NYPD for five years, he sure got it, but the biggest adventure was still to come! Brogan suggested that they both apply for the exchange programme with Demeter City and Haldane grasped the opportunity with both hands.

A man of action and popular in the department

Haldane loves action, but take care if you go out on patrol with him, Cadet - sometimes he gets a little bit carried away. Despite this, he is one of the best liked officers in the DCPD and he knows how to enjoy himself. Haldane is a good friend to have and he has a good understanding of space technology, so he'll be able to help you with almost every aspect of your new job.

FREEZE FRAME

EXIT

PUTER CLONE

13

SURVIVING...
The Space Suburbs

High above the surface of Altor, in the "uptown" area of Demeter City, are the Space Suburbs. These orbiting residential suburbs house a large number of the city's "professional classes" - not necessarily wealthy people, but mostly those in employment who have enough disposable income to afford the rents, which are a great deal higher than for accommodation downtown.

PUTER ART

rather dilapidated Suburbs exist, however, as do some especially luxurious ones.

A typical Space Suburb

Residents of the Space Suburbs live in "houses" and "apartments" of various sizes, many with attractive gardens, containing lawns and flowers, from which they can observe fabulous views of the stars and the planet Altor below. The central hub houses a public park and other basic amenities, although most residents commute daily to bigger stores and their places of work downtown.

From up-market to the very top

Although they are all considered more desirable places to live than almost anywhere on the surface, there are various grades of Space Suburbs. The average Suburb is clean and well-maintained, with many features making life there more comfortable and enjoyable. A few poorly maintained and

SCROLL OUT

Altor InfoNet

SURVIVAL TIP: IF YOU'RE STAYING ON ALTOR FOR LONG, THEN APPLY FOR AN APARTMENT IN A SPACE SUBURB AS SOON AS YOU CAN - LIFE'S A LOT SAFER IN ORBIT THAN IN DOWNTOWN DEMETER.

JANE CASTLE
BIO-FILE

Rank: **Officer**
Serial No: **DCPD H4289F**
Species: **Human**
Home: **Demeter City**

An expert on aliens and their environment

If you're confused by life in Demeter, then Jane Castle is the officer to talk to. She grew up in England and studied languages before spending some time with the European Community Police Force. Even though she transferred to the DCPD little more than a year before Brogan and Haldane, Jane knows far more about the aliens of Demeter City and the environment they inhabit.

Living in downtown Demeter

While many of her human colleagues live in the Space Suburb, Jane Castle chooses to share a converted warehouse in Demeter City itself with her tarn partner and close friend, Officer Took. Jane claims to have a boyfriend back on earth, but - and this is between me and you, Cadet - that may just be what she tells Jack Haldane to make it easier to resist his regular advances!

FREEZE FRAME

Assistance Required

PUTER ART

"Brogan! Haldane!" barked Captain Podly. "My office - now!" The two officers were busy consuming well-earned cups of coffee back at Space Precinct 88 when they heard the call.

"What does he want now?" groaned Jack Haldane. "We've been working for eight hours straight. Can't we even have a five minute break?"

"Come on, Haldane." Patrick Brogan downed his drink in one and stood up. "I guess the criminals around here don't take coffee breaks." They made their way to the Captain's office in time to see Sergeant Fredo coming out of the room, examining a strange green-hued ring.

"What's that, Fredo?" grinned Haldane. "Thinking of proposing to wife number four?" Fredo just sighed, shook his head and went on his way. He was used to Haldane's irreverent sense of humour and, while the humans at the Precinct usually found him funny, Fredo

wasn't always amused. When Brogan and Haldane finally entered the office, Captain Podly was looking rather agitated and was accompanied by a young Cadet.

"Good of you to come, gentlemen," said Podly. "Perhaps I can interest you in a bit of police work?"

"What's going on?" asked Brogan, ignoring the Captain's sarcasm.

"Well, you know that spate of freighter hijacks we've had lately?" explained Captain Podly. "I was just reviewing the evidence in the case with Sergeant Fredo when a report came in to say that another one has gone missing. I want the two of you to find that freighter and catch the criminals before they get the chance to empty the fuel out of it."

"We're on it, Captain," nodded Brogan, making for the door. "Can you download any further details to the on-board computer in our cruiser?"

"Consider it done, Lieutenant," confirmed Podly. "There's just one other thing." Brogan and Haldane stopped in their tracks. "You're going to need some assistance out there. I've assigned one of our brightest cadets to join you on this mission. Good luck!"

You accompany Brogan and Haldane to their police cruiser and all three of you head for the scene of the latest freighter hijack. Information relating to the case is fed into the cruiser's computer and Haldane is able to calculate a projected

PUTER ART

course for the freighter after the hijack.

"According to this information, the freighter was just about to complete a long haul flight when the crime was committed less than a quarter of an hour ago," Haldane informs Brogan. "Should be a piece of cake to pick up its trail if we hurry." Speeding on, the cruiser comes into view of the freighter within a few minutes. It has crash-landed onto the surface of Altor, where it rests, mostly undamaged.

"Looks like our missing freighter," says Brogan, as the police cruiser swoops down upon the scene. "Let's check it out - but be careful, the hijackers have either abandoned it or they've crashed it by accident. Either way, there's every chance they're still around." You stay behind the two more experienced officers as they approach the freighter, but soon discover that the only person on board is the human pilot. He is bound and gagged and seems very pleased to see you.

"Thank goodness!" gasps the pilot, as Haldane undoes his restraints. "I thought I was done for there. I was attacked by this gang of aliens - creons I think they were - and they took over the freighter, tying me up while they stole the fuel I was carrying." Brogan takes you out to inspect the freighter's fuel tank from the

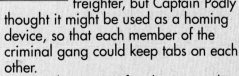

outside. You find a circular hole punched into it some 200 millimetres in diameter.

"The hijackers have drained the freighter's fuel cargo dry, Cadet," says the Lieutenant. "Looks like they used some kind of high pressure suction device to empty the tank through this hole. They must've worked quickly, since there's no sign of them - or any of the fuel - now!" When you go back inside the freighter, Haldane shows you something he has found on the floor near the controls of the craft.

"Look at this!" he exclaims. "A weird green ring, like the one Fredo had back at the Precinct." You are able to tell him a bit about the other ring, because the Captain and the Sergeant had been looking at it with you before Brogan and Haldane had arrived. Apparently, the ring was designed to emit a high frequency signal. Fredo had suggested that it might have been used by one of the previous hijackers to sabotage the controls of a freighter, but Captain Podly thought it might be used as a homing device, so that each member of the criminal gang could keep tabs on each other.

"Whatever it's for, this ring is the second one of its kind to turn up at the

"Can I be of assistance?" asks Slomo. You consider the facts for a moment. Perhaps Slomo can uncover some important details relating to the freighters themselves. He helps you to access the station's mainframe computer and run some questions on it:

HOW MANY FREIGHTER HIJACKS HAVE THERE BEEN?
SEVEN. INCLUDING TODAY'S CRIME.
DO THE FREIGHTERS ALL BELONG TO THE SAME COMPANY?
NO. ALL SEVEN ARE OWNED BY DIFFERENT COMPANIES.
HAS THE STOLEN CARGO BEEN FUEL EACH TIME?
YES.
HOW MUCH FUEL DOES AN AVERAGE FREIGHTER CARRY?
27.678 MILLION CUBONS.
LIST SPECIFICATIONS OF TYPICAL FUEL TANK.
TEMPERATURE TOLERANCE RANGE 20K-473K.
MAXIMUM CAPACITY 29.336 CUBONS.
FILLING HATCH 0.5 METRE x 0.5 METRE.
DESIGNED FOR LONG HAULS 20 HOURS-2600 HOURS.
CONSTRUCTION: TITANIUM ALLOY WITH ALTORIUM.
DETAIL FILLING OPERATION.
HIGH PRESSURE PUMP IS USED TO PUMP FUEL INTO TANK.
PROCESS IS COMPLETED WITHIN 97 MINUTES.

scene of a hijack," muses Brogan, taking the electronically enhanced piece of jewellery from Haldane and pocketing it. "That almost certainly makes it an important clue to solving these crimes - if we can work out how it fits in." After calling out a repair team to work on the freighter and then dropping the obviously shaken pilot off at Demeter's closest medical facility, you return to Precinct 88 with the others to report your findings and review the evidence.

"So you let them get away," Captain Podly growls at Brogan, when he explains what has happened.

"It wasn't like that, Captain," protests Haldane. "It was as if they were never there. We caught up with the freighter less than half an hour after the hijack took place and they were already gone."

"Yes, and so was the fuel!" snorted the Captain. After a considerable amount of ear-bashing from Podly, you all leave his office to pursue the case further, though you fear that the trail is going cold already. Brogan and Haldane decide to go off and make some further enquiries, in an effort to discover where the mysterious ring might have come from. They leave you at the station to consult Slomo for any more information which might be useful.

"How's it going, Cadet?" a voice suddenly interrupts your examination of the computer information. It is Officer Romek. You tell him you think you are making some progress, but there are a few things about the case that you still don't understand. Romek has brought you the first ring to check over. "Fredo reckons you might learn something from a closer look at this," he tells you. "It's a silly thing if you ask me. I mean, if it's supposed to be a ring, you'd think they'd make it big enough to fit on your finger!" Romek laughs as he tosses it over to you.

You take a close look at the ring. It is green with a crudely etched, unidentifiably alien symbol on it. You find that you can slip it onto your finger easily enough, but you take it off quickly as green is definitely not your colour!

You return to the computer, but find it hard to think of anything else to ask it, so you shut down the terminal and thank Slomo for his help.

"I'm happy to help, Cadet," Slomo assures you.

"Find out anything important, kiddo?" asks Haldane. He and Brogan have just returned to the Space Precinct, but are none the wiser as to the origin of the rings. In fact, the "alien symbol" bears no relation to any known language or culture. You fill in your colleagues on your own investigations and hand the ring back to Lieutenant Brogan. He stares at it for a moment and even slips it on and off his own finger.

"Of course!" gasps Brogan. "The solution to this case is right under our noses. I think it's about time we made a few arrests." He leads you and Haldane back out to the police cruiser and you speed off downtown.

BROGAN HAS MANAGED TO WORK OUT WHO IS BEHIND THE SERIES OF HIJACKINGS. HE ALSO KNOWS EXACTLY HOW THE CRIMES WERE CARRIED OUT AND WHAT THE SIGNIFICANCE OF THE RINGS IS. HAVE YOU MANAGED TO PUT ALL THE EVIDENCE TOGETHER AND COME UP WITH A THEORY OF YOUR OWN?

THE SOLUTION

The culprits responsible for these crimes are the pilots themselves. Nothing said by the pilot in this latest hijacking makes any sense. He suggested that a gang of creons had attacked him and extracted the fuel in his cargo tank - all within 30 minutes! You know that the hole through which the fuel was stolen is much smaller than the regular filler hatch. Given that the usual filling operation takes some 97 minutes, it is reasonable to assume that the extraction process would take at least that long and probably much longer. There wasn't time to empty the tank, yet all the fuel had gone. Impossible, unless the fuel had already gone **before** the "hijack" took place. It could be that the tanks were never filled, in which case the whole thing could be an insurance scam

- but this seems unlikely since all seven freighters belonged to different companies. Assuming that the tanks were full at the start of the journey then, this indicates at least some complicity from the pilots involved in the hijacks, as the fuel has undoubtedly been removed slowly through the punctured hole during the freighter's long haul.

The rings, which were found at the scene of two of the crimes were assumed to have been dropped by the alien hijackers. The alien symbols on them seemed to back this up, but on investigation they bore no resemblance to any known alien culture - let alone the creons'. Indeed, the rings would not even fit on the finger of a creon (Officer Romek), so it is more likely they were made to be worn by humans, then disguised as "alien jewellery".
In fact, the rings were worn by the freighters' pilots and contained signalling devices for their accomplices to home in on during the actual theft of the fuel. The hijacks were then staged to cover the pilots' backs, but they got careless on two occasions and failed to properly dispose of the rings. The criminals were not too worried, however, since they had taken the precaution of disguising them with the alien symbols and believed the rings would not be linked to the pilots anyway, but would instead help back up their stories. All the clues point to the pilots, then, probably working as a gang to commit the crimes. No doubt they will reveal whether they have any other accomplices working with them when you bring them into the Space Precinct for interrogation.

TEST ENDS ✓

19

Alien File

CREONS

One of the main differences between policing some ordinary "quiet" precinct - say in downtown New York or Chicago - and working the streets of Demeter City is the presence of all kinds of aliens. The two main alien races on Altor are the creons and the tarns. Both groups outnumber the human population considerably, so you'll need to understand them and have some idea how to deal with them before you can go out on patrol without supervision.

Physically large with incredible vision

The second thing you'll notice about a creon is his or her large physical stature - larger indeed than most humans or tarns of a comparable age and sex. The first thing you'll notice is, of course, their incredibly large eyes. Many humans find the creons' physical appearance something of a shock on first sight, but the aliens use their facial features to remarkable effect. To a creon, a human's inability to manipulate his or her eyes to provide 360° vision is a distinct disadvantage. They can even watch two entirely separate things at once - an immensely valuable skill on the streets of Demeter City.

FREEZE FRAME

The migration from Danae

Creons originally come from the Planet Danae in the Mentorn System. Life is very hard on Danae and the lure of a better life on another world proved a tremendous incentive to leave the place. As members of a very outgoing and enterprising race, many migrant creons were attracted to the varied trading opportunities afforded them on Altor and a large creon community soon grew up in Demeter City.

Superstitious and ritualistic

One thing the creons have brought from their home planet of Danae is a strong sense of ritual. They are very keen on doing things their own way and intensely dislike having their routines upset, particularly by non-creons. This adherence to ritual stems from the fact that creons are extremely superstitious and quite literally fear breaking with the centuries' old traditions of their race.

FREEZE
FRAME

SURVIVAL TIP: NEVER UNDERESTIMATE A CREON - THEY ARE AN ADAPTABLE AND INTELLIGENT RACE. IN FACT, MANY OF YOUR BEST COLLEAGUES ARE CREONS, INCLUDING YOUR BOSS AT PRECINCT 88!

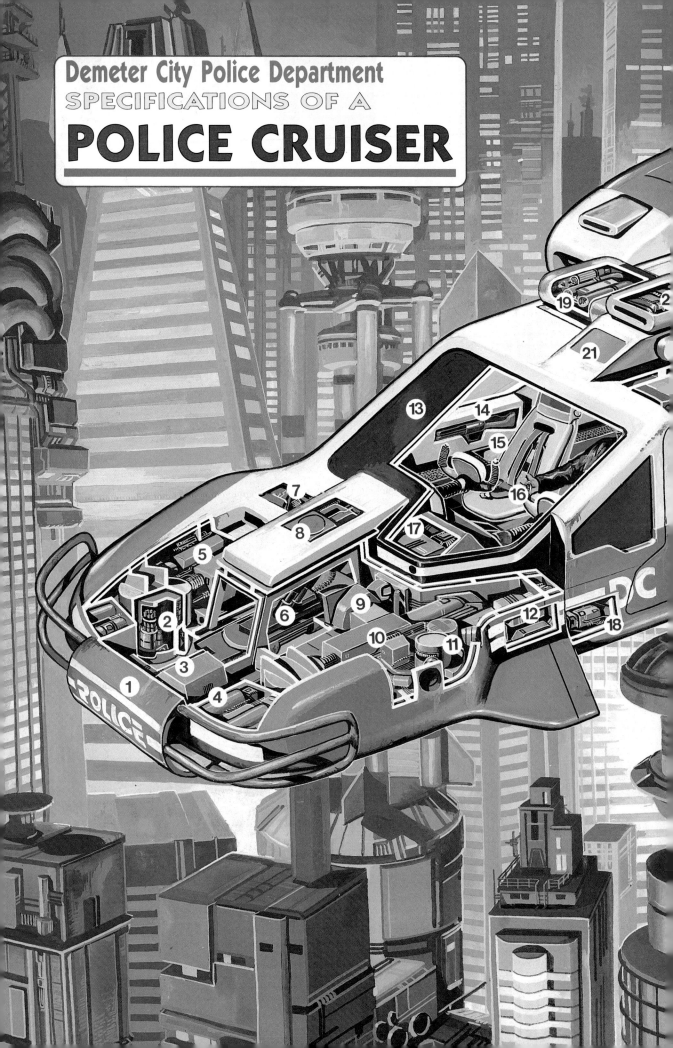

For **Police Cruiser** Tek-Spec, scroll onto the next page...

TEK-SPEC OF SPACE CRUISER

1 Heat resistant bodywork constructed from plastic mixed from polymers, co-polymers, ceramic and cahelum additives: trade marked as CoPamic (TM).

2 Retracted starboard Energy Pulse Gun (EPG).

3 Heatshield sensor analysis computer.

4 Headlights - incorporating range-finding and target-hunting lasers.

5 Starboard manoeuvring thruster fuel tank.

6 Forward landing leg (retracted).

7 Air filter (closed when in space).

8 Forward docking beam guidance sensor.

9 One of three electromagnetic clamps connecting cabin escape pod to the rest of the cruiser.

10 Emergency back-up computer.

11 Port manoeuvring rocket-thrusters.

12 Port magnetic clamp incorporating connectors from the emergency to primary computer.

13 Polarised heat-resistant windshield, admiting light but absorbing ultra-violet and infra-red, dissipating heat from laser fire and solar radiation.

14 Door mounted riot gun.

15 Medical pack.

16 Dual-control ergonomically simplified steering console.

17 Primary super-computer.

18 Cabin escape pod thruster.

19 Lighting array incorporating self-focusing lasers for audio-video communication.

20 Klaxon / sub-space beacon.

21 Emergency solar energy panel.

22 Flexible seating (automatically moulds itself to fit alien as well as humanoid body forms).

23 Previn Coil Superconductor generates artificial gravity within the vehicle and provides downward electro-magnetic force during take-off.

24 Life support conduits.

25 Electro-magnetic clamp and cabin escape pod thruster.

26 Micro-fusion reactor.

27 Port landing leg (retracted).

28 Liquid oxygen tank.

29 Aft docking frame (allows a Hyperdrive Booster Unit to be coupled to the vehicle for interstellar travel).

30 Port liquid hydrogen tank.

31 Sub-space communications array.

32 Air inlets (closed for space flight).

33 Ramjet turbine.

34 Compressor.

35 Combustion chamber / heat exchanger.

36 Combined rocket and jet engine nozzle.

37 Liquid hydrogen regulator - pumps fuel to nozzle for space travel.

38 Laser mountings ignite liquid hydrogen which creates explosive motive force for vehicle.

39 Manoeuvring thrusters.

40 Emergency short-range rockets.

41 Life Support System (LSS) incorporating zyolithic crystals to prevent condensation, and algae to siphon carbon dioxide out of the cabin.

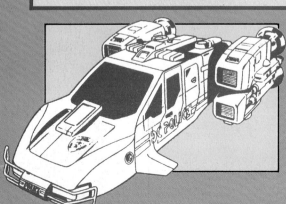

AURELIA TOOK
BIO-FILE

Rank: Officer
Serial No: DCPD T3993F
Species: Tarn
Home: Demeter City

Level-headed and always willing to help

Born and raised in Demeter City, Officer Took - or "Tookie" if you get to know her well - joined the DCPD when she was 18. She is popular at the Precinct because she goes out of her way to help friends - particularly her partner, Jane Castle, who she lives with downtown. As a Tarn, Took has a "third eye" which enables her to read minds and move objects through telekinesis.

FREEZE FRAME

TOOK

FREEZE FRAME

SLOMO

Rank: R.S.A.
Serial No: DCPD R0562N
Species: Robot
Home: Space Precinct

Purpose built R.S.A.
(robotic secretarial assistant)

Slomo is Precinct 88's robotic office "gofer", capable of fulfilling all manner of secretarial duties and a lot more besides. He is programmed to take notes at meetings, draft letters, file and retrieve data, and even to fetch coffee. However, if you're like the other officers, then you'll probably soon have him playing Slamball or some other game instead of fulfilling his normal duties!

25

◉Alien File

TARNS

Many of the problems you may encounter as a police officer working out of the 88th Precinct stem from the uneasy interaction of the many aliens who live on Altor. The two main alien races on Altor are the creons and the tarns, both of whom consider themselves to be somewhat superior to the other. You will need to understand both groups well before you are fit to police the streets of Demeter City with any real hope of success.

Leaving Simter for Altor

Simter is the tarns' home planet in the Mentorn System and the vast majority of the population there were severely afflicted by poverty. For this reason there was a mass exodus from the planet and tarns were among the first settlers on Altor, helping to found Demeter City. Highly intelligent and quick to adapt to their new environment, the aliens soon carved out new lives on their adopted planet, fulfilling all kinds of important roles in a developing society. The tarn community is vital to the political and economic well-being of Altor, but you might find them less than forthcoming - perhaps even shy - when you are investigating a crime.

FREEZE FRAME

The power of the third eye

Although they are a very private race, tarns have astounding abilities that make them extremely useful when it comes to crime detection. By opening their third eye and concentrating hard, they are able to move objects with the power of telekinesis and even to read minds. It takes many years for a young tarn to master these abilities and most never do. In fact, for many of them, this power is very hit and miss and using their third eye results in frequent and often quite acute embarrassment for the tarn in question.

A credit to the force

Those tarns who have even partial success at harnessing their telekinetic talents have a tremendous advantage in interpersonal relationships - making them extremely good police officers. It is hard for a criminal to lie to a cop who can read their mind any time he or she wants to!

PUTER CLONE

SURVIVAL TIP: JUST BECAUSE A TARN'S THIRD EYE IS SHUT, DON'T ASSUME THEY CAN'T DETERMINE YOUR TRUE INTENTIONS OR FEELINGS. THEY ARE A VERY PERCEPTIVE AND INTUITIVE RACE.

New York? Chicago? So you think some of your earth cities are tough and crime-ridden, do you, Cadet? Well, welcome to Demeter City - Crime Capital of the Galaxy! We've got crimes here they've never even dreamed of in those earthbound police precincts. And if you're going to survive here for very long, you will have to familiarise yourself with some of the most common ones.

Organ Legging

PUTER ART

SURVIVAL TIP: THE GANGSTERS BEHIND SNUFF FIGHTING ARE VERY DANGEROUS, SO THEY MUST BE INVESTIGATED WITH CAUTION. GENUINE HELP MAY BE SOLICITED FROM "ENSLAVED" FIGHTERS.

While this crime is not unique to Demeter City, the variety of alien life forms on Altor make it a particular problem here. "Organ legging" - the gruesome practice of stealing organs from the bodies of unfortunate victims for illegal transplant purposes - is rife among the poorer communities in downtown Demeter and is generally masterminded by gangs operating out of Danae.

SURVIVAL TIP: MOST VICTIMS OF THIS CRIME ARE DRUGGED BEFORE THEY ARE MURDERED FOR THEIR ORGANS. EFFICIENCY AND URGENCY DURING AN INVESTIGATION MAY SAVE LIVES.

Extortion

Snuff Fighting

Battling to the death in an arena for the enjoyment of an audience, "snuff fighters" ply a strictly illegal trade in Demeter City. Naturally enough, most of these fighters are outcasts or illegal immigrants and are far from willing participants in underground bouts organised by unscrupulous criminals, but are forced into participating in this barbaric form of "entertainment".

Some of the Galaxy's most vicious and accomplished extortionists operate on Altor - mostly targeting the many and varied business concerns which run successfully out of Demeter City. In this age of high-tech explosive devices, it is particularly hard to prevent a determined extortionist - such as the infamous Snake - from carrying out their threats if their demands for money are not met.

Alien Smuggling

With Demeter City's population growing too fast for comfort, immigration is carefully controlled - resulting in a large number of disgruntled aliens who are unable to gain legal citizenship on Altor. Not surprisingly, Demeter's criminals have been quick to cash in on this demand by setting up smuggling rings, illegally bringing aliens into the city - for a price!

Counterfeiting

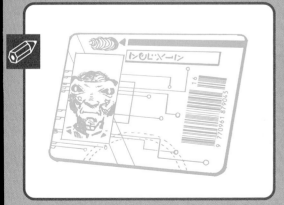

Some of Demeter's counterfeiting operations follow the traditional lines of producing fake currency - various forms of tokens and paper money from different planets are used in the downtown markets - but the most lucrative side to this business is the creation of false identity tags. Exceptional criminal expertise is required for this, but a fake tag is a prized possession indeed.

Drug Trafficking

Drugs cause problems all over the Galaxy, but nowhere more so than on Altor. With myriad different species living on the planet, the effects of drug abuse are unpredictable and highly dangerous. For example, HE-11 - otherwise known as "Flash" for obvious reasons - was sold on the streets of Demeter City and actually provoked spontaneous combustion in its users!

♣ Rookie Logic

You've made it so far, Cadet, but now you have to prove you can use your brain! If you want to become a fully fledged cop you're going to need to have your wits about you, so see if you can solve the puzzles on these pages.

1. How observant are you? Look at these six things:

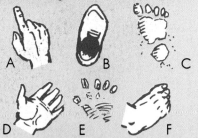

Can you deduce which one is the odd one out and why?

3. How ingenious are you? Arrange six coins like this:

Now move just one coin so that you have two lines, each with four coins in it.

2. The message below looks like it's written in some alien language, but it's not - it's in code. Decipher it quickly, Cadet - someone's life might depend on it!

UIJT JT B DPEFE NFTTBHF GSPN
CSPHBO. NFFU NF PO TLBMM
TUSFFU SJHIU BXBZ, UIFSF'T HPJOH
UP CF USPVCMF.

4. Any good at riddles, Cadet? Read this and see if you can identify what is being described:

The beginning of eternity,
The end of time and space,
The beginning of every end,
The end of every place.

6. You know what an anagram is - but can you identify your colleagues?

(a) CHALK JEAN AD
(b) A CLEAN JEST
(c) PARROT BACKING
(d) PLENTY OXROD
(e) OI TAKE RAOUL
(f) SMOKERS AIL

5. Take nine matches and lay them out in three triangles like this:

Now make five triangles by moving just three of the matches. This should tell us just how cunning you really are!

Alien File

Armand Loyster
From MELAZOID

Definitely different!

"Different" is how Captain Podly describes this particular business executive, hailing originally from Melazoid One. Loyster could also be described as "grotesque", since - like all melazoids - he is covered with a thin, blue slime which sticks to everything he touches. His habit of catching flies with his tongue and the horrible smell which surrounds him also fail to enhance his image, but Loyster remains an amiable family man and a law abiding citizen.

Enil Kmada
MEKI

Legendary killer returned to life

The legend of the Meki tells of a race whose souls were lost and condemned to live out their lives in host bodies. A Meki needs life-force to survive, so while it can hibernate for many years without its host even knowing it is there, when it grows hungry it awakes to feed... and to kill! A century ago, the Great Purge saw all the Meki hosts fired into the suns in an attempt to rid the worlds of their evil, but one Meki - Enil Kmada - survived.

Vachel
ULRED

Beast-like messenger of doom

As a native of Nevin Three, Vachel is beast-like in appearance and has piercing predator eyes. These fearsome attributes belie the spirit and compassion which brought him to Altor, since his main desire on that occasion was to warn the people of Demeter City against the threat of the Omera - an evil nomadic race who had reduced his own world to civil war and had plans to invade Altor itself!

Wirt
CLYBEN

Well armed for a life of petty crime

As a Clyben, Wirt has a unique advantage over other pickpockets - he has an extra pair of arms! Despite this, his life of crime has never really paid off and he still lives rough on Paradise Street in one of Demeter City's roughest neighbourhoods. Consequently, he has tried out many other crimes he is less well-equipped for and you will find extensive entries on him under petty theft and even hopper stealing on the Precinct 88 crime database.

The Snake
SPECIES UNKNOWN

A ruthless extortionist

The Snake is a member of a little known reptilian species and his ugly, scaly appearance belies an even uglier personality. He is wanted across the star system for terrorising at least seven planets and has one simple message for his victims - "Pay or die!" Those who refuse to heed his warning are likely to receive one of his intricately wired bombs, packed with Semtel explosive and micro-welded together with his own yellow acid blood!

End Report...

VR TEST 2

The Perfect Crimes

PUTER ART

"This is ridiculous!" snapped Officer Jane Castle, as she accessed the files on a string of robberies committed in downtown Demeter via the on-board computer link-up in her police cruiser.

"What's wrong, Jane?" asked Officer Took, who was piloting the cruiser on their way to investigate a newly reported robbery at the Demeter Bank.

"We've got eight unsolved robberies on the Precinct's files with the same reported M.O. as this one," explained Jane. "The trouble is, there are absolutely no witnesses to any of the crimes - and nobody has any idea how they were perpetrated."

"That makes no sense," Took pointed out. "If so little is known about the robberies, how did they manage to link them back at the Precinct?"

"But that's exactly the point, Tookie," said Officer Castle. "Each of these crimes is so perfect, they must be connected. The criminal's M.O. seems to somehow carry out his crimes without anyone seeing or hearing anything while he does it. Haldane's already started calling him the 'Nowhere Man', because it's like he's invisible or something." When they arrived at the bank, the story was the same.

"Everything seemed normal," sighed the bank manager, "then suddenly I noticed that the vault was open and all our precious mineral ore reserves had vanished." Took and Castle looked carefully around the crime scene, but there were no obvious clues. Climbing back into their police cruiser, they started a routine sweep of the area - looking for anyone who might look at all suspicious. Suddenly, Brogan's face appeared on their communication screen.

"Get yourselves back to the Precinct, Officers," he told them, "I think we may have a lead on the case and the Captain wants you to check it out." When they arrived back at Precinct 88, Brogan explained that a scientist working for TimeCorp Interplanetary had called in to report two separate crimes that he believed were both carried out by the mysterious 'Nowhere Man'. "I think he may have some important information for us," Brogan continued. "Take our young Cadet here along with you and see what the three of you can find out. Podly wants this case cracked - and quick!"

Officers Castle and Took take you along to the plush headquarters of TimeCorp

Interplanetary. The scientist, a brilliant tarn named Alberiol Chenk, escorts you all up to his laboratory where the two robberies took place.

"This is our most advanced research lab," he tells you. "We have some of the most remarkable technology in the Galaxy here at TimeCorp. Our security is normally very good, but we had a break-in in this lab about two weeks ago..."

"What makes you think the perpetrator was our 'Nowhere Man'?" asks Jane Castle. "I gather that the break-in was quite a conventional one."

"That's right," says Chenk, "but the second one fits the pattern perfectly and I think the two break-ins are connected." He explains that a small experimental device was stolen during the first robbery and that a quantity of tachyon cells were taken during the second. "The technology we're working with here is highly confidential," he goes on, "but I can tell you that the stolen device is powered by our special patented tachyon cells. I think that whoever took it needed more tachyon cells to make further use of it."

"Do you have another one of these devices, Dr Chenk?" Officer Took asks him. The scientist nods. "Perhaps we might learn something by taking a look at it, then," suggests Took. Chenk fetches the device. It is about the size of a pocket calculator and he warns you all not to touch the buttons.

While Castle asks the scientist to suggest any possible suspects for the crime, you and Took examine the device. Despite the warning, you can't resist pushing one of the buttons on it. Fortunately, nothing happens, but you do feel a strange sensation. Everything and everyone around you seems to have frozen and Officer Castle has stopped talking in mid-sentence. Then you notice that Castle has started speaking again and Took is asking you if there's anything wrong. You shake your head to assure her that you're fine and all three of you are soon on your way to continue your investigations.

"Dr Chenk reckons there are three main suspects for the break-in at TimeCorp," Jane tells you, as you climb back into the police cruiser. She takes the pilot's seat and gives you and Took her notes to look at. "If one of these suspects does turn out to be the

TimeCorp thief, he could well be our mysterious 'Nowhere Man', too," she insists.

Jane's notes read as follows:

EFLARD RITCHENT - Melazoid. Works for the rival company, Relativity Incorporated. He has made several attempts to gain access to TimeCorp's secret research on black holes.

AGIAL LURT - Tarn. A young student, he recently joined TimeCorp as a lab assistant. Has been off sick since the first break-in. He has the necessary access codes to have breached TimeCorp's security.

CLINTON ESTLIN - Creon. Time-Corp's former security chief. He left the company under a cloud two months ago. Knows TimeCorp's security system inside out.

"First stop - Relativity Incorporated," says Jane, as she lands the police cruiser some time later. The three of you ask to see Eflard Ritchent, but the receptionist tells you he's not around. Took is suspicious and insists that she will wait for him while you and Castle go off and check on the other suspects. Clinton Estlin's apartment is nearest, so you head there.

"It looks like Mr Estlin is in anyway," says Jane, pointing to the distinct shadow of a creon through the apartment's window, as you walk up to the door. You depress the door sensor and wait for a reply. There is none. You try again, but there is still no answer. "I don't think he wants us in there," says Jane. "Time we took a look inside..." You help her to break down the door, but when you enter the apartment, it is completely empty. No sign of Clinton Estlin, nor any furniture or other personal possessions.

"It's like he moved out weeks ago," you observe. "So how come we saw someone in here just a few seconds ago?" You accompany Jane to Agial Lurt's shared accommodation in a redeveloped warehouse not far from where Castle and Took live. Unfortunately, there is no sign of him either.

"It's really not our day, is it?" shrugs Jane. Stopping only to put out an APB on all three suspects, you head back to Relativity Incorporated to pick up Officer Took. While you've been away, however, there has been a startling development.

"I was fed up with waiting," Took explains when you arrive, "so I sneaked into Ritchent's office, only to find that he had been there all along. Not only that, but Agial Lurt was with him, discussing the research going on at TimeCorp!" It transpires that Lurt is not sick at all, but has agreed to come and work for Relativity Incorporated. Much to the pair's annoyance, Took has arrested them both on suspicion of involvement in the 'Nowhere Man' crimes.

"Let's take them back to the Space Precinct," says Castle, "we can interrogate them further there." You all return to Precinct 88 and receive a message on route from Orrin and Romek.

"We've picked up your man," Orrin informs you. "We spotted Estlin down-town and we're just bringing him in."

"I'm not sure we need him," Took says to Castle. "It's obvious that our criminal is one of these two. All we need to find out now is how the 'Nowhere Man' committed his crimes."

"It might be worth questioning all three suspects, Tookie," Jane replies, "I have an idea how the 'Nowhere Man' manages to carry out his remarkable robberies and I'd like to hear what they all have to say about that."

YOU KNOW JUST AS MUCH ABOUT THE CASE AS OFFICERS CASTLE AND TOOK - PERHAPS A LITTLE BIT MORE. THEY BOTH BELIEVE THE INVESTIGATION IS ALMOST OVER. SO CAN YOU IDENTIFY THE 'NOWHERE MAN'? AND HAVE YOU GOT ANY IDEA HOW HE COMMITS HIS APPARENTLY PERFECT CRIMES?

THE SOLUTION

The 'Nowhere Man' is indeed one of the three suspects. His first crime was the theft of the small device at TimeCorp. As you found out when you touched it, this device somehow distorts time - freezing everything around you while you are still free to move. Using this device, the 'Nowhere Man' was able to walk straight into places like the Demeter Bank and take as long as he wanted to rob the place and make his getaway. Nobody could see him do this as time was frozen for them and they knew nothing about it. Dr Chenk was right in thinking that the criminal needed the tachyon cells to power the device, hence his second raid on the TimeCorp lab.

So which of the three is the guilty man? They all have a motive for getting at TimeCorp, although Eflard Ritchent and Agial Lurt were rather more interested in industrial espionage than committing robberies. They may well have charges to answer, but Clinton Estlin is the 'Nowhere Man'. He gave himself away when you and Officer Castle arrived at his apartment. Estlin didn't realise you had seen him, so he activated the time distortion device and froze time while he made his getaway - along with all his possessions, including the proceeds of his many robberies.

TEST ENDS ✖

PUTER CLONE

SURVIVING...
Demeter City

Altor InfoNet

Populated by an assortment of aliens originating on dozens of different planets, Demeter City is the strangest and probably the most dangerous place you're ever likely to patrol in this or any other universe! If you want to succeed as a cop here, or even to survive very long, then you'll have to learn as much about the place as you can - starting right here...

A city in three dimensions

An extraordinary place, Demeter is quite literally a "three dimensional city", since it extends from the ground right up into space, as well as covering a sizeable portion of Altor's surface. Orbiting space suburbs and towering penthouses provide housing for many in what is often described as "uptown" and the higher above ground you live, the more "upmarket" you are.

> **SURVIVAL TIP:** MANY OF THE CITY'S RESIDENTS FEEL A CERTAIN AMOUNT OF RESENTMENT TOWARDS THOSE WHO LIVE IN UPTOWN. LOOK OUT FOR POSSIBLE FLASH POINTS AND KEEP A LID ON THEM.

Commerce, culture and crime

Demeter is the largest city on Altor and has become a thriving centre for commerce as the planet's reputation as a major inter-stellar refuelling and trading outpost has grown. A remarkable mixture of alien cultures, the city is a uniquely suitable environment for intergalactic business - unfortunately, too much of that "business" is conducted by Demeter City's many criminals!

> **SURVIVAL TIP:** LOTS OF DEMETER'S CRIMINALS OPERATE IN GROUPS, LIKE THE INFAMOUS HYDRA GANG. NEVER TRY TO TAKE ON ONE OF THESE GANGS ALONE - ALWAYS CALL FOR BACK-UP.

Downtown Demeter

At the other end of the scale is "downtown" - the part of Demeter which is actually on the ground! This is the main commercial centre of the city, but as a residential area it is strictly downmarket. Your temporary quarters are in downtown Demeter, Cadet, so watch it! Most of the city's low-lifes operate out of this area, so at least you'll be on hand if a crime is reported!

> **SURVIVAL TIP:** STAY ALERT WHEN YOU'RE IN DOWNTOWN DEMETER AND TRY NOT TO GET LOST! OFFICER CASTLE IS THE PERSON TO APPROACH FOR FURTHER ADVICE, AS SHE KNOWS THE AREA WELL.

HUBBELL ORRIN
BIO-FILE

Rank: Officer
Serial No: DCPD C3857M
Species: Creon
Home: An older rundown Space Suburb

A young officer with a natural wit

Officer Orrin is known for his sense of humour, but he also has a tendency to be lazy and loves to play games. He was born and raised in Demeter and still lives with his parents in an older and more dilapidated Space Suburb in the crowded orbit of Altor. Orrin is normally partnered by Officer Romek, but he is occasionally teamed with Beezle, a fellow creon officer with an insane streak!

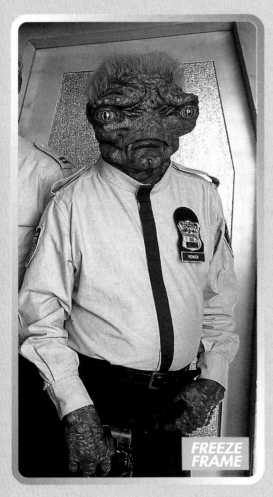

SILAS ROMEK
BIO-FILE

Rank: Officer
Serial No: DCPD C3848M
Species: Creon
Home: Demeter City

Member of a well respected police family

Officer Romek's grandfather was one of Demeter's first cops, so space policing is very much in his blood. Despite this, he is not always happy in his work. Romek's low sense of self-esteem stems from his difficulty in measuring up to his family's high expectations and he often finds himself caught up in his partner Officer Orrin's grandiose schemes.

39

SPACE PRECINCT 88
SECURITY CODE 2

You've done well in your practical tests and routine assessments, Cadet. Now you have to sit your final exams. If you pass, you will be ready for your next stage of training as a police officer at a Space Precinct. If you fail the exam, however, you'll be working your way back to your home planet on a passing space cruiser - leaving your badge and uniform behind! The exam is in three parts designed to test you on all aspects of what you have (hopefully) learnt in your time at Precinct 88. Good luck!

SECTION A

POLICING DEMETER CITY

1. You are patrolling the streets of down-town Demeter when you meet a member of the Hydra Gang. Do you:
(a) arrest him because he is bound to have committed a crime
(b) keep your eye on him because he may well commit a crime
(c) run away in case he commits a crime against you!

2. The Snake is in town and you track him down. He appears to be wounded with cuts to both his arms. Do you:
(a) slap the cuffs on him and take him back to the Precinct
(b) call an ambulance to take him to the hospital
(c) keep him covered while you call for some back-up.

3. You are working undercover and discover a horde of smuggled items in an abandoned warehouse. Five angry looking tarns suddenly appear and ask you what you are doing. Do you:
(a) tell them you are a cop and that they are under arrest
(b) tell them you have come to read the meter
(c) distract them to give you time to escape and seek help

4. You are downtown when you encounter a clyben who claims to have been mugged and knocked to the ground. Do you:
(a) leave him to sit on the ground as you question him and obtain a description of the assailant
(b) help him up and then question him
(c) decide he looks a dodgy customer and carry on.

5. You notice a hopper speeding away from the Demeter City Bank. Do you:
(a) ignore it because any sensible bank robber would have invested in a better getaway vehicle
(b) chase after the hopper and overtake it as quickly as possible
(c) follow the hopper at a safe speed, then order its occupants to stop via your external speaker.

6. You have just come off duty and are heading home for a well-earned rest when you come across a crime in progress. Do you:
(a) call in a crime report to the Precinct so that someone else can handle it
(b) turn a blind eye - after all, you can't stop every crime in Demeter
(c) announce that you're a cop and attempt to make an arrest.

SECTION B

DEDUCTIVE REASONING

1. Space Precinct 88 is in turmoil. A major criminal has escaped from Asteroid A5 - otherwise known as "The Rock". Captain Podly has three officers available - Orrin, Romek and you - but he can only spare one of you to track down the convict. Podly knows that this will be a very tough assignment, so he wants to make sure he sends the most intelligent and resourceful among the three of you. He decides to test each of you before he makes his decision.

Calling you into his office, the Captain asks you and your fellow officers to put on blindfolds. Orrin wants to know what this is all about, but Captain Podly assures him that everything will soon become clear. While you are wearing the blindfold, Podly puts a cap on your head and you hear him say:

"Each of you is now wearing either a black or a white cap. When I remove your blindfolds, I want each of you to raise your hand as soon as you see a black cap. You can drop your hand again when you can tell me the colour of your own cap."

The Captain then takes your blindfold off and you see that both Orrin and Romek are wearing black caps. You put your hand up as Captain Podly instructed you to and so do your fellow officers. All three of you exchange puzzled glances for a few minutes while you consider the problem.

Will you be the first to drop your hand and tell the Captain what colour the cap is on your head? Don't just guess, because he will want you to outline your reasoning before he gives you the assignment.

2. You are on patrol with Officer Haldane in downtown Demeter when you encounter a tarn female arguing with two creon males. You both investigate what is going on and Haldane tells you that he knows the creons quite well - they are both petty thieves. The woman is angry because one of them stole her bag earlier on and she has just recognised them on the street. Haldane asks you to interrogate the creons to try and find out what happened.

The first one, Lenial Prusk, tells you: "Extrell snatched the bag. All I did was run off with it!"

The second creon, Extrell Blog, insists: "I did snatch the bag. But Lenial did not run off with it."

Knowing the creons, Officer Haldane tells you that one of them will lie completely, while the other will lie exactly half of the time. He can't tell you which will do what today, but he has found a witness to the crime while you were questioning the suspects. A human female called Terri Parks saw the whole thing, but she is also well known at Precinct 88 and Haldane informs you that she lies exactly half of the time as well.

"I saw Lenial snatch the bag," Terri tells you. "Then Extrell ran off down the street with it."

Taking into account all three statements, can you work out what actually happened so that you can arrest the guilty party or parties?

SECTION C

GENERAL KNOWLEDGE

1. Which police force did Officer Jane Castle work for before she transferred to Space Precinct 88?

2. What is Brogan's wife called?

3. Where was Captain Podly born?

4. Who is Officer Orrin's usual partner?

5. Slomo is an RSA - what do the letters stand for?

6. Which lifeform constitutes the third biggest community on Altor?

7. How many arms does a typical clyben have?

8. Name the evil nomadic race which threatened to invade Altor.

9. Who was the slimy blue-skinned melazoid Captain Podly once described as "different"?

10. What planet do Ulreds come from?

11. What is the standard cop's vehicle in Demeter City?

12. Where do Lieutenant Brogan and his family live?

13. What must citizens of Demeter carry at all times?

14. What exactly is "downtown Demeter"?

15. What kind of criminal was the nake?

16. What is the tarns' home planet called?

17. In what remarkable ways can a creon use his or her eyes?

18. In what even more remarkable ways can a tarn use his or her third eye?

19. What is the creons' home planet called?

20. Who is Officer Jane Castle's tarn partner?

ASSESSMENT:

SECTION A

1. (a) 1 point, **(b)** 4 points, **(c)** 0 points - stay vigilant, but you won't be able to arrest everyone you meet

2. (a) 0, **(b)** 1, **(c)** 4 - the Snake's blood is deadly acid, so watch yourself

3. (a) 1, **(b)** 0, **(c)** 4 - many tarns can read your mind, so don't try to lie to them, but don't bite off more than you can chew either!

4. (a) 4, **(b)** 1, **(c)** 0 - never ignore a cry for help, but be on your guard - this is a typical pickpocket's ruse

5. (a) 0, **(b)** 1, **(c)** 4 - don't over-react, they probably aren't bank robbers at all, but remember that speeding is an offence, too

6. (a) 1, **(b)** 0, **(c)** 4 - you may be off duty, but you're still a cop and immediate action is often the most effective

SECTION B

(8 points for each correct answer)

1. The cap you are wearing is black. If you had been wearing a white cap, then both Orrin and Romek would have seen it on your head, as well as the black cap on their partner's. Since they both put their hands up, they each knew that the other could see at least one black cap. If it wasn't the one on your head, they would have instantly known it was the one on their own. As neither of them put their hand down again to announce their conclusion, it is safe for you to assume that your hat is not white and it is therefore black.

2. Lenial snatched the bag and he ran off with it, too. Lenial and Extrell agree that Extrell snatched the bag, but since one of them lies completely, the culprit must be Lenial. As this is what Terri tells you, her other statement must be false, so Lenial also ran off with the bag.

SECTION C

(1 point for each correct answer)

1. European Community Police Force
2. Sally
3. Skall Street in downtown Demeter
4. Officer Romek
5. Robotic Secretarial Assistant
6. Humans
7. Four
8. Omera
9. Armand Loyster
10. Nevin Three
11. Police Cruiser
12. Space Suburb
13. Identity tags
14. The part of the city that is actually on the ground
15. An extortionist
16. Simter
17. To provide 360° vision and to watch two things at the same time
18. To move things by telekinesis and to read people's minds
19. Danae
20. Officer Took

YOUR RATING:

51-60 points - *An outstanding performance. You've learnt your lessons well during your short spell at Precinct 88. The next stage of training looks like being a formality for an able rookie cop like yourself.*

31-50 points - *Well done, you're ready to proceed with your training. Don't look too pleased with yourself, though, Cadet, there is significant room for improvement and you'll find that things get even tougher from now on!*

11-30 points - *Oh, dear. You really haven't been paying attention, have you? Policing Demeter City really is one of the toughest assignments in the Galaxy, so you're going to have to resit this stage of your training again.*

1-10 points - *Get packing, Cadet, there's a transport leaving for earth first thing in the morning. Are you any good at shining shoes?*

OFFICIAL SEAL ✱ ✱ ⊙

Congratulations! You've completed your first tour of duty at Space Precinct 88. Now it's time to meet your boss:

REXTON PODLY
BIO-FILE

Rank: Captain
Serial No: DCPD C1641M
Species: Creon
Home: Space Suburb

A stickler for correct police procedure

You've made a good impression so far, Cadet, but you'd better keep on the right side of Captain Podly. While he is very proud and protective of his squad, nothing infuriates him more than when his officers mess up. Not a believer in "hunches", Podly demands more from his officers - so make sure you get some hard evidence before you bring in those criminals!

An experienced cop and well respected in Demeter

Having been born on Skall Street, in one of Demeter's worst neighbourhoods, Rexton Podly joined the DCPD at the age of 19. Working his way up the ranks during more than 30 years on the force, he was eventually promoted to Captain and is highly regarded by all his colleagues. Without doubt, Podly is a hard taskmaster, but he is also a brilliant and incisive decision maker.

COMPETITION
FREE FROM VIVID IMAGINATIONS

115
GREAT PRIZES MUST BE WON!

- ⬡ 5 extra large and highly detailed Space Cruisers
- ⬡ 10 drama-packed detective board games
- ⬡ 20 Lieutenant Brogan 12" tall action figures
- ⬡ 30 sky-racing Police Bikes
- ⬡ 50 superb mini action figures

These terrific prizes are on offer to humans everywhere (sorry, creons and tarns!).

Vivid Imaginations have created a range of action figures, weapons and accessories vital to self-preservation in space. In fact, there is everything you need to create your very own **SPACE PRECINCT** adventures.

And, when the going gets tough and the tough need to get going, Vivid Imaginations have just what the **SPACE PRECINCT** team ordered for some serious space travel! The **DEMETER CITY POLICE BIKE** comes with firing laser cannon while the futuristic **POLICE CRUISER** includes electronic lights and sirens, laser cannon and even a super secure jail trap to keep those evil villains locked away. Both the **DEMETER CITY POLICE BIKE** and the **POLICE CRUISER** are scaled to accommodate the mini action figures.

For would-be Demeter City detectives seeking strategic excitement in space, then

the **SPACE PRECINCT CRIME BUSTERS BOARD GAME** is not to be missed. You assume the role of one of the **DCPD** and make your way around the board in a series of strategic leaps an bounds. Accumulate your clues, then... **BUST THE BAD GUY!**

So, if you don't want to come back to Earth with a bump, make it your mission to enter our great competition! All you have to do to be in with a chance of winning one of these **115** fabulous **Space Precinct** prizes is answer the following question:

Which planet is home to the Tarns?

Write your answer on a postcard - or the back of a sealed envelope - together with your name and address. Then stick on a stamp and send it to the following address:

Vivid Imaginations Space Precinct Annual Competition,
Newsstand Services
Office Block 1
Southlink Business Park
Southlink
Oldham OL4 1DE

The closing date for entries is 31st January 1996. Prize winner names will be drawn at random and matched up with prizes by the editor. No correspondence will be entered into. A list of winners will be available from 14th February 1996.
Employees, relatives and agents of Grandreams, Vivid Imaginations, Norton and Company and Newsstand Services are not eligible to enter.